Point to each letter as you sing "The Alphabet Song."

Aa Bb Cc Dd Ee Ff Gg

Hh Ii Jj Kk

Ll Mm Nn Oo Pp

Qq Rr Ss

Tt Uu Vv

Ww Xx

Yy and Zz

Now I
know my ABC's.
Next time won't you
sing with me?

Trace and write the letter.

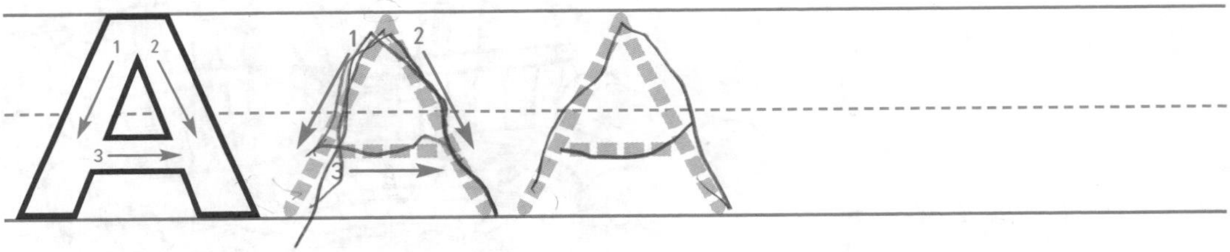

Circle the ones that begin with A.

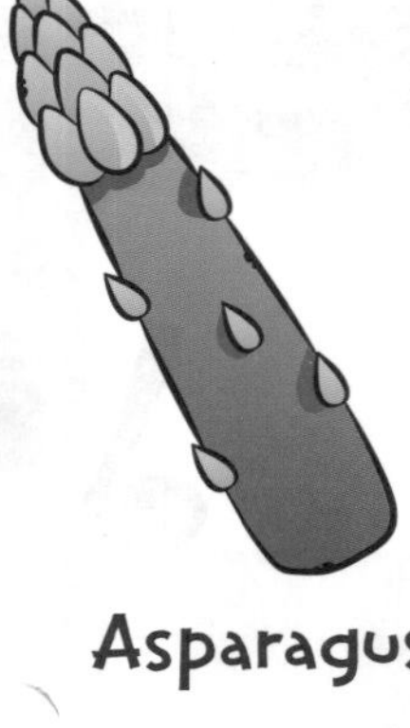

Asparagus

Apple

Lemon

Trace and write the letter.

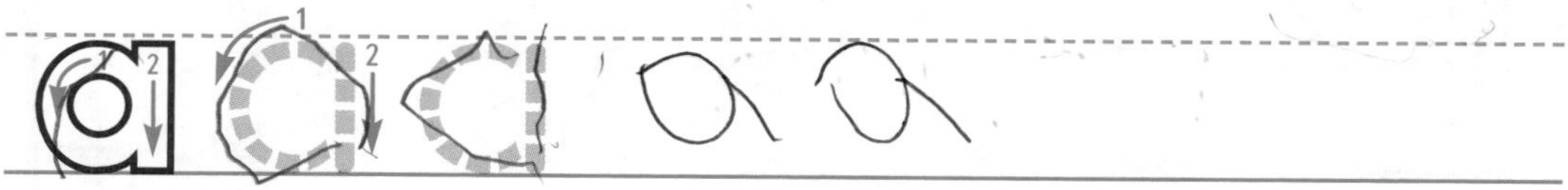

Circle the ones that begin with a.

butterfly

ant

alligator

Trace and write the letter.

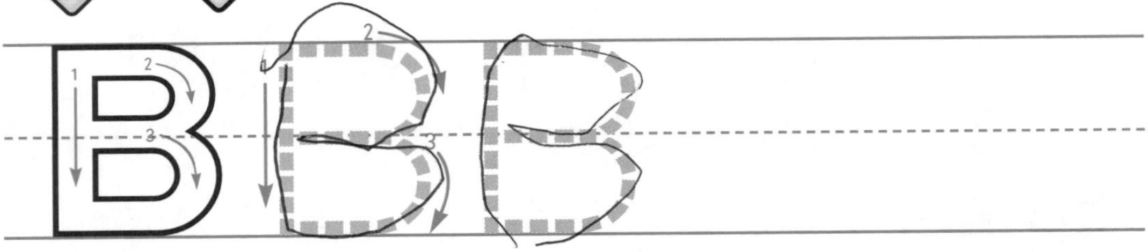

Circle the ones that begin with B.

Basketball

Whistle

Bowling Ball

Lowercase b

Trace and write the letter.

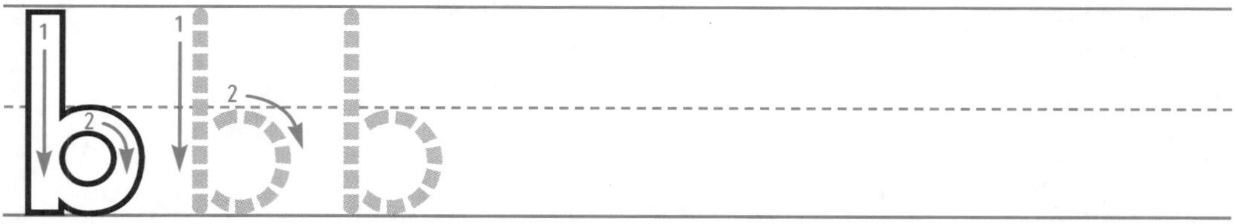

Circle the ones that begin with b.

bear

bee

giraffe

Trace and write the letter.

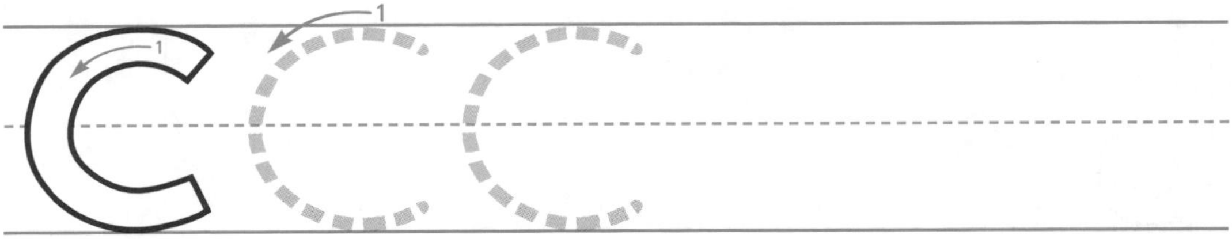

Circle the ones that begin with C.

Sailboat

Car

Cart

Lowercase c

Trace and write the letter.

Circle the ones that begin with c.

cupcake

dog

cow

Capital D

Trace and write the letter.

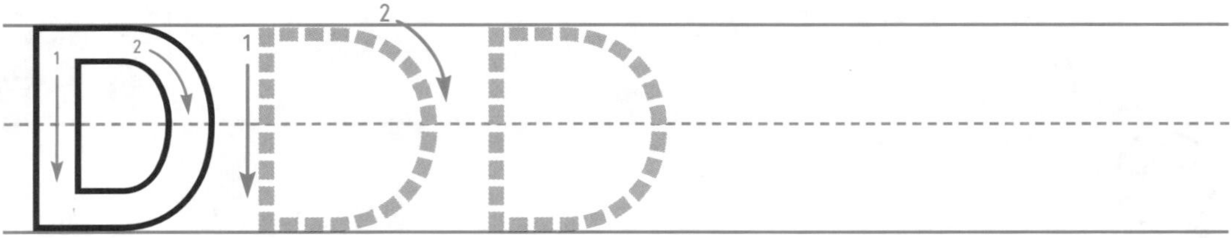

Circle the ones that begin with D.

Duck

Lion

Dog

Trace and write the letter.

Circle the ones that begin with d.

dog

elephant

duck

Trace and write the letter.

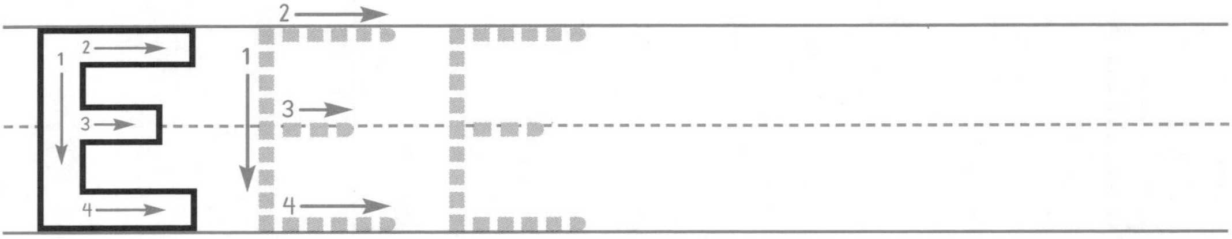

Circle the ones that begin with E.

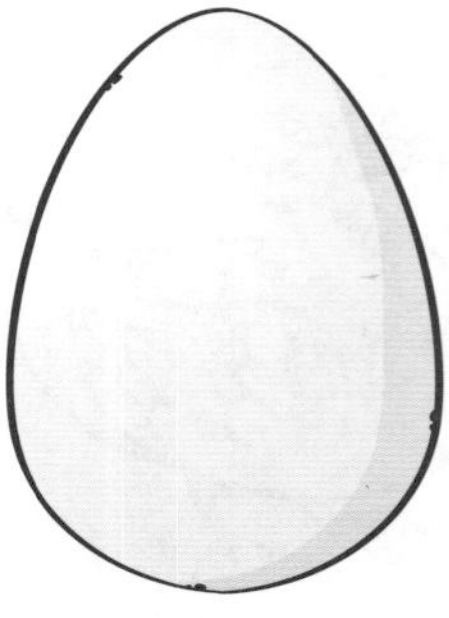

Egg

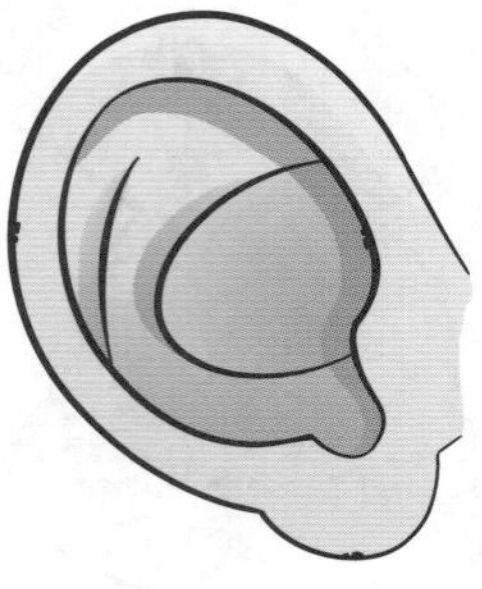

Ear

Clown

Trace and write the letter.

Circle the ones that begin with e.

sheep

elf

elephant

Trace and write the letter.

Circle the ones that begin with F.

Three

Four

Five

Lowercase f

Trace and write the letter.

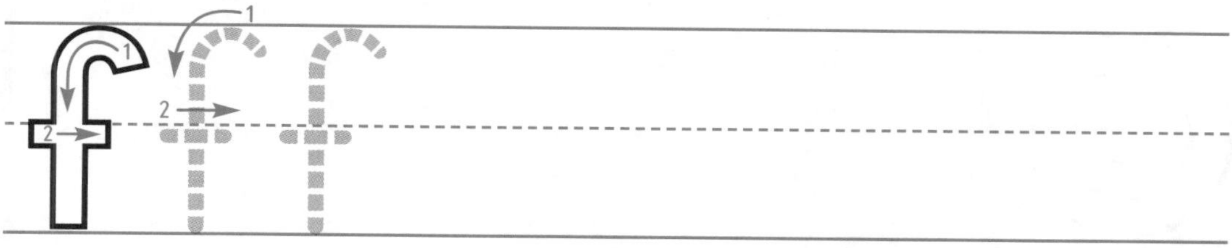

Circle the ones that begin with f.

fireman

farmer

kite

Trace and write the letter.

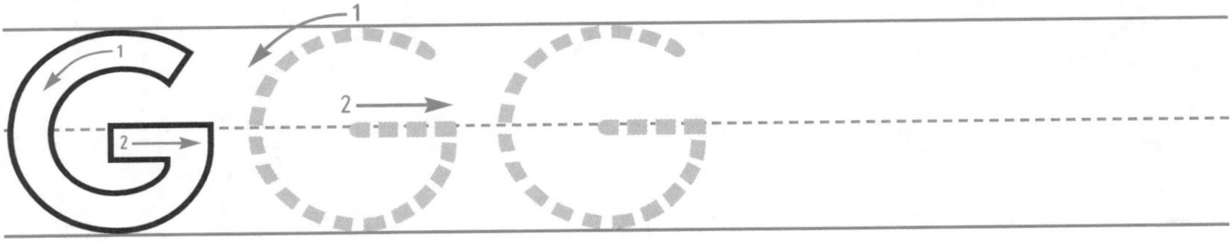

Circle the ones that begin with G.

Guitar

Corn

Gate

Lowercase g

Trace and write the letter.

g g g

Circle the ones that begin with g.

gumballs

girl

circus

Capital H

Trace and write the letter.

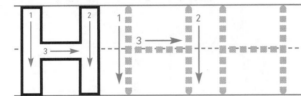

Circle the ones that begin with H.

Horse

Mouse

Hen

Trace and write the letter.

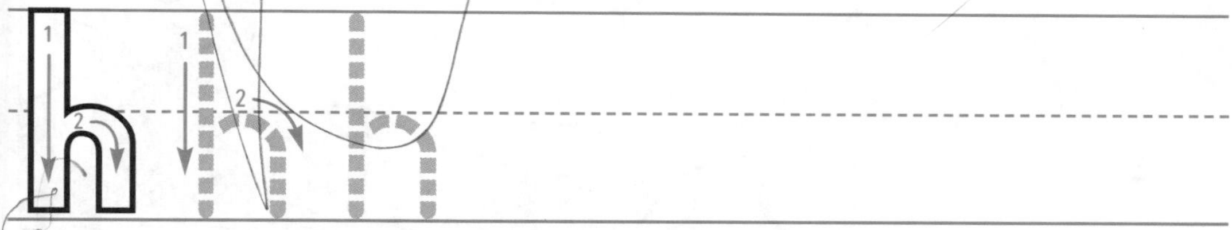

Circle the ones that begin with h.

house

barn

hen

Color the picture using the color code.

A = B = C =

Connect the dots from A to H.
Color the picture.

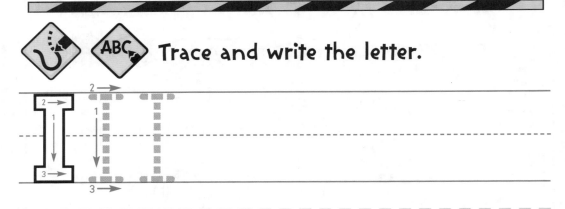

Trace and write the letter.

Circle the ones that begin with I.

Indian

Squirrel

Iguana

Lowercase i

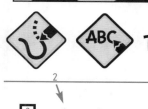

Trace and write the letter.

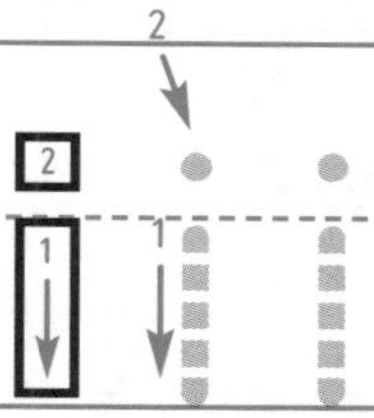

Circle the ones that begin with i.

ink

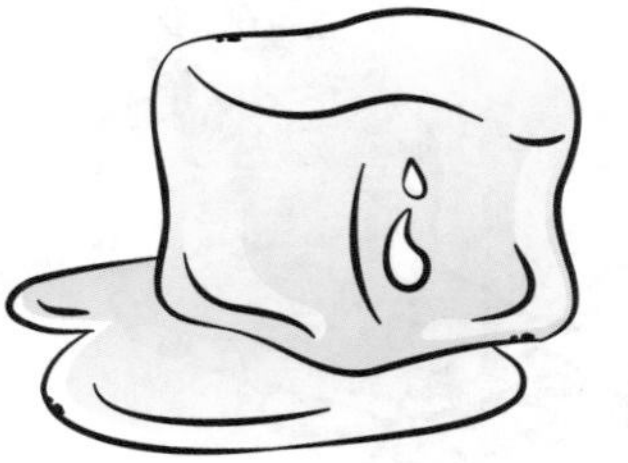

ice

frog

Trace and write the letter.

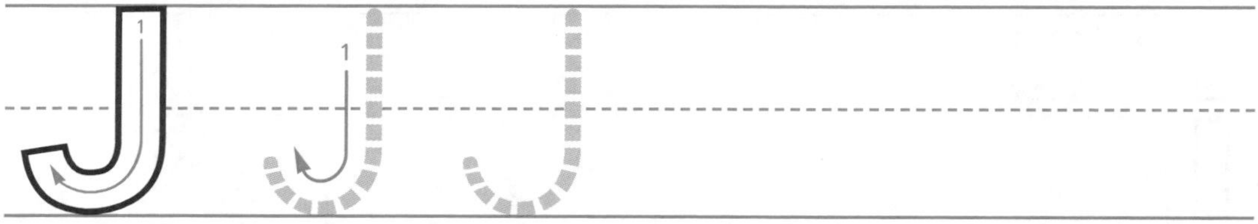

Circle the ones that begin with J.

Milk

Jam

Juice

Trace and write the letter.

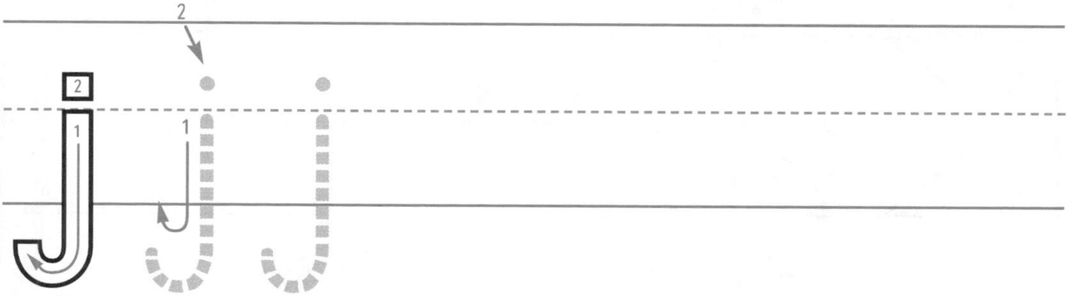

Circle the ones that begin with j.

jack-o-lantern

fox

jacks

Trace and write the letter.

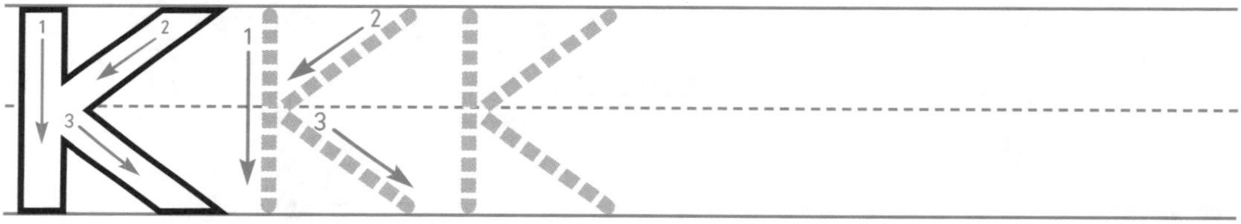

Circle the ones that begin with K.

Snail

Kitten

Koala

Trace and write the letter.

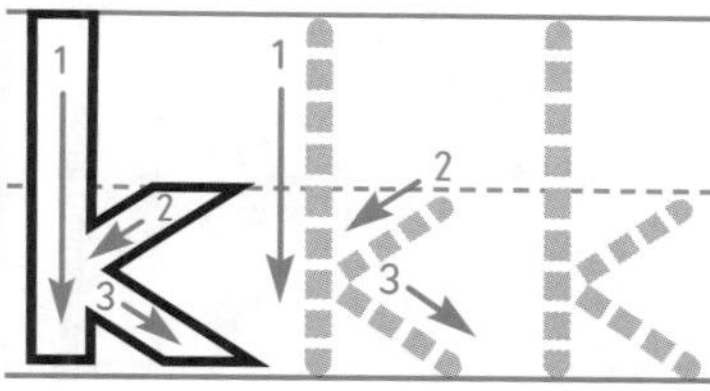

Circle the ones that begin with k.

bird

kangaroo

king

Capital L

Trace and write the letter.

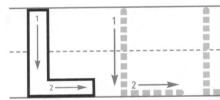

Circle the ones that begin with L.

Lamb

Lion

Grasshopper

Trace and write the letter.

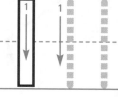

Circle the ones that begin with l.

lemon

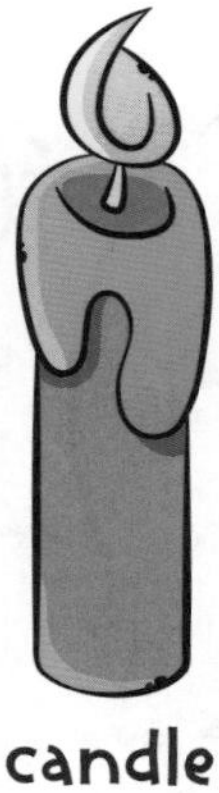

candle

lamp

Connect the dots from A to K.
Connect the squares from a to k.
Color the picture.

Connect the dots from a to l.
Color the picture.

Trace and write the letter.

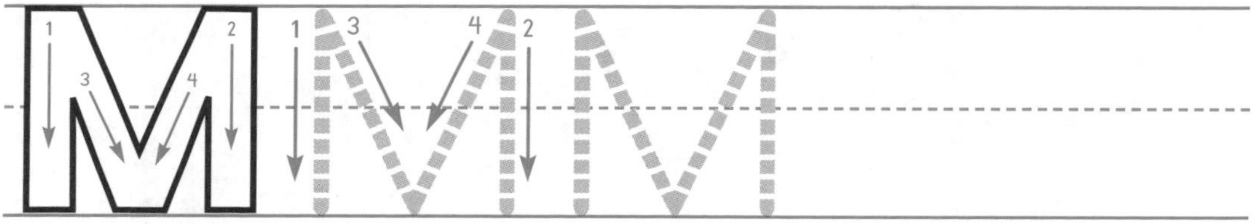

Circle the ones that begin with M.

Giraffe

Mouse

Monkey

Trace and write the letter.

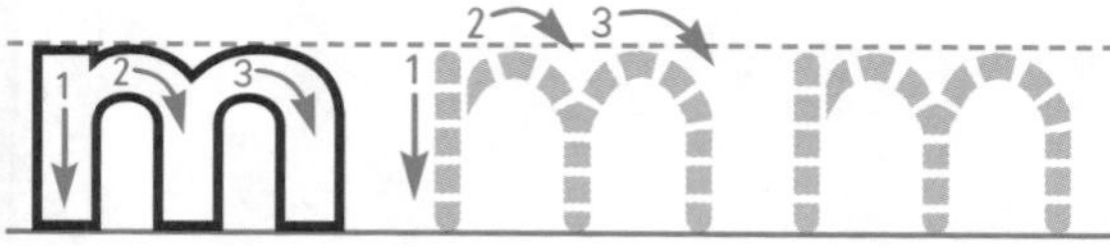

Circle the ones that begin with m.

rabbit

monkey

moon

Capital N

Trace and write the letter.

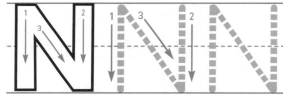

Circle the ones that begin with N.

Notebook

Nurse

Chick

Trace and write the letter.

n n n

Circle the ones that begin with n.

nest

fish

necklace

Trace and write the letter.

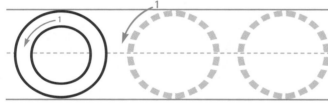

Circle the ones that begin with O.

Otter

Squirrel

Owl

Trace and write the letter.

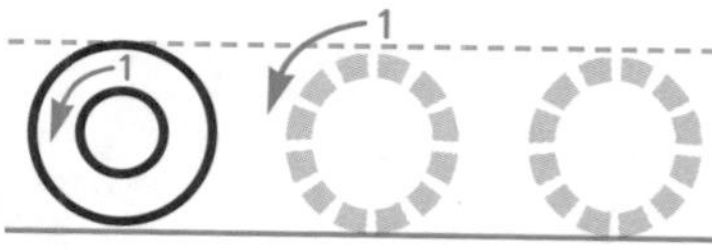

Circle the ones that begin with o.

bird

octopus

ox

Trace and write the letter.

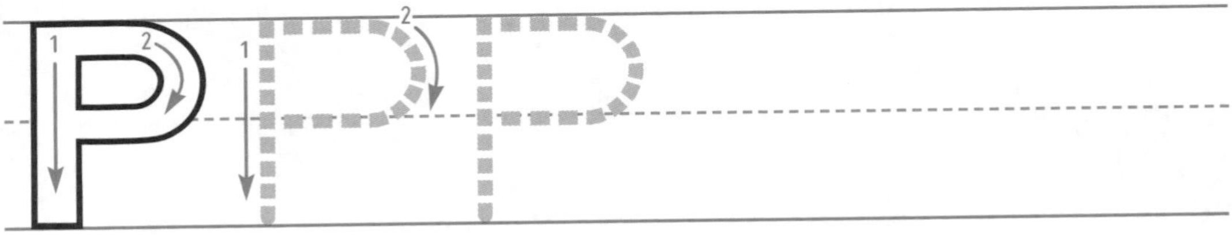

Circle the ones that begin with P.

Pizza

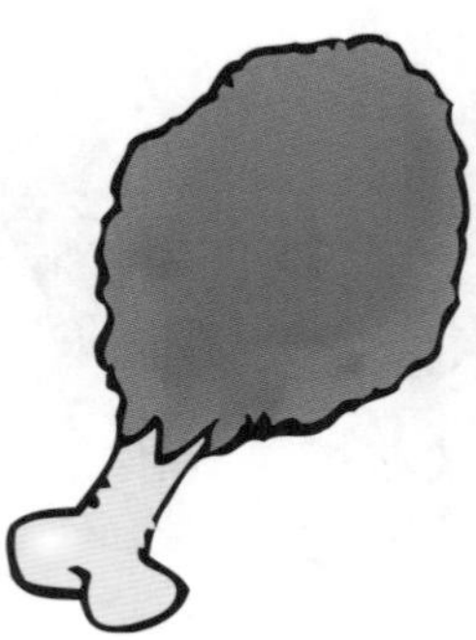

Chicken

Pineapple

Lowercase p

Trace and write the letter.

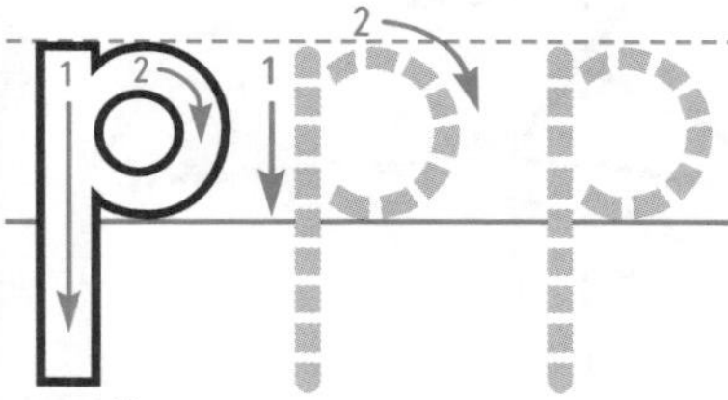

Circle the ones that begin with p.

parrot

frog

porcupine

Connect the dots from A to O.
Color the picture.

Draw the path to the pot of gold by following the letters from I to P.

Capital Q

Trace and write the letter.

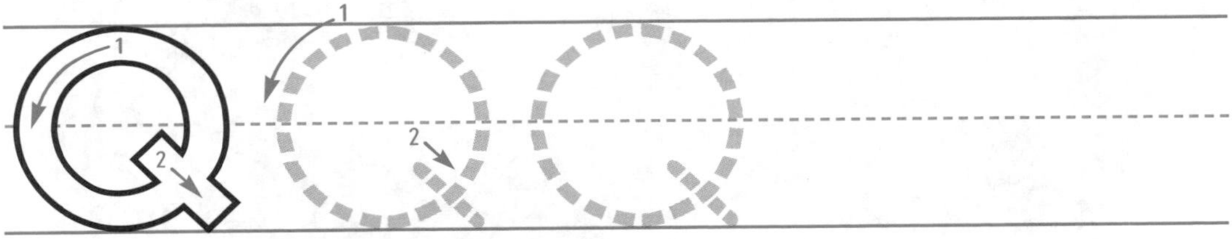

Circle the ones that begin with Q.

Quarter

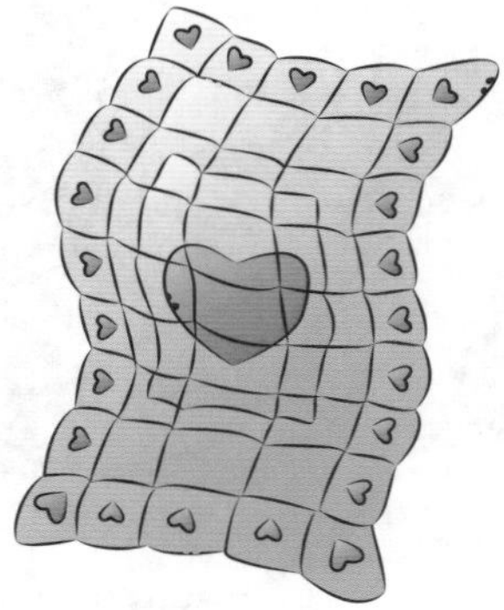

Quilt

Necklace

Trace and write the letter.

Circle the ones that begin with q.

queen

frog

quarter

Trace and write the letter.

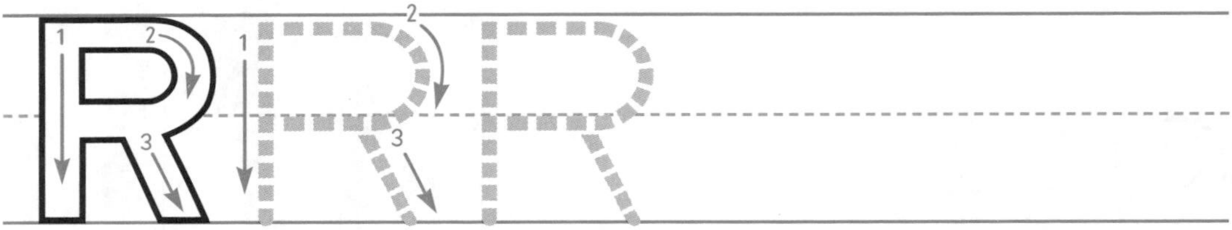

Circle the ones that begin with R.

Rake

Rocket

Plane

Lowercase r

Trace and write the letter.

r r r

Circle the ones that begin with r.

robot

boy

rocket

Trace and write the letter.

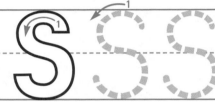

S S S

Circle the ones that begin with S.

Sailor

Seal

Crab

Trace and write the letter.

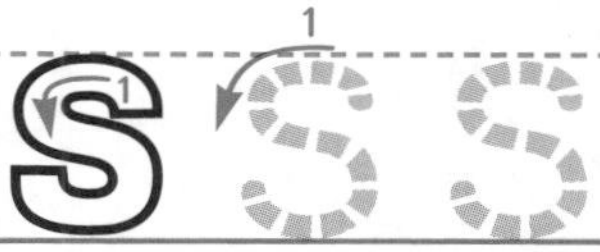

Circle the ones that begin with s.

seal

sun

doll

Capital T

Trace and write the letter.

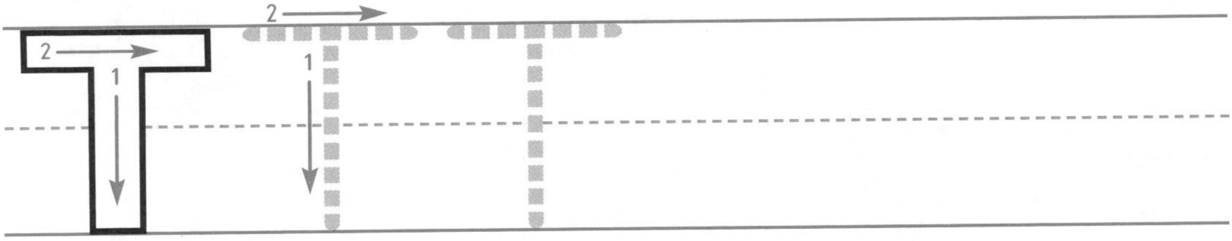

Circle the ones that begin with T.

Skateboard

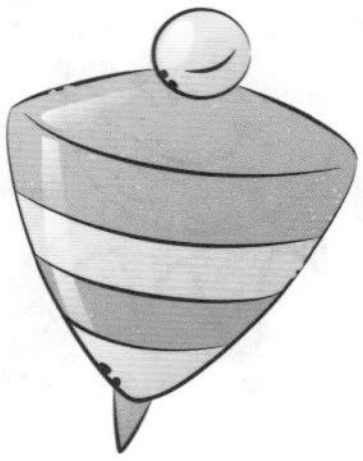

Top

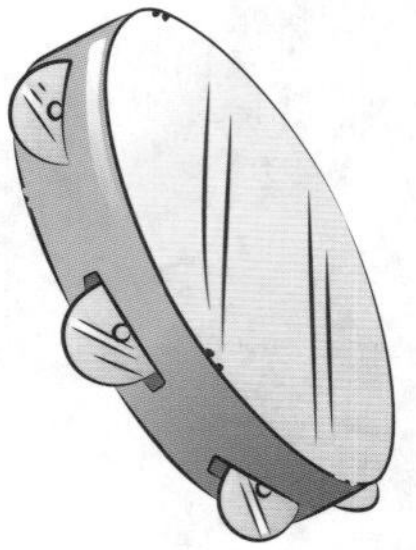

Tambourine

Lowercase t

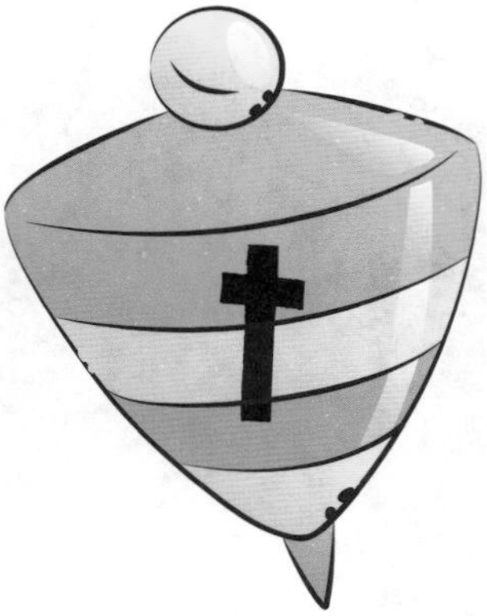

Trace and write the letter.

Circle the ones that begin with t.

turtle

turkey

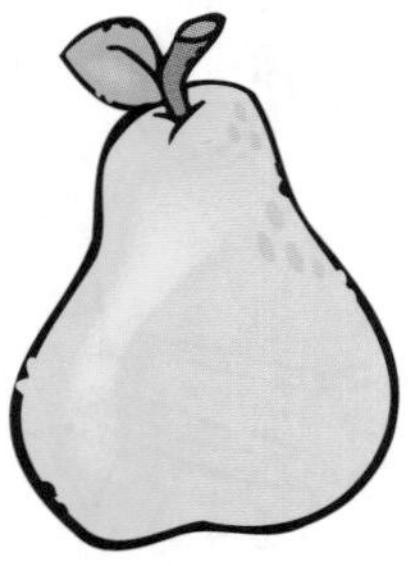

pear

Capital U

Trace and write the letter.

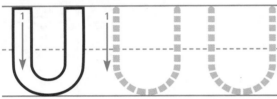

U

Circle the ones that begin with U.

Underwear

Umpire

Frog

Trace and write the letter.

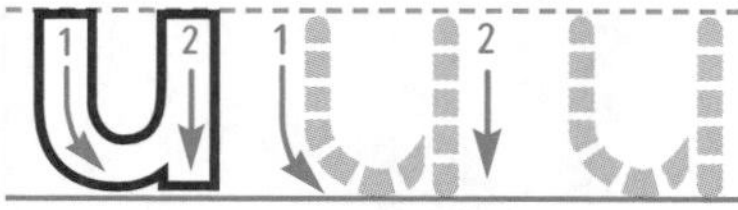

Circle the ones that begin with u.

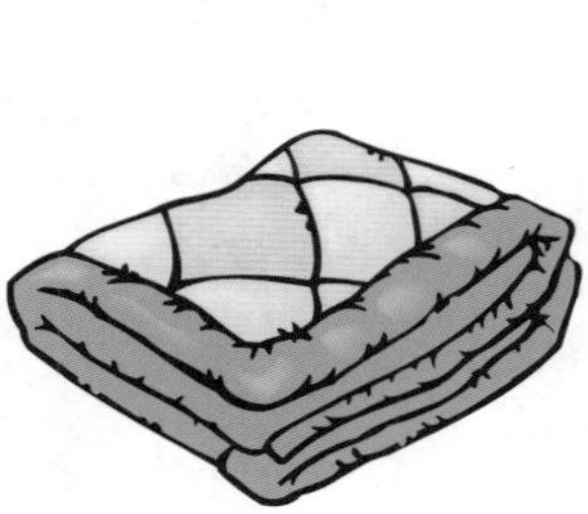

blanket

umbrella

underwear

Capital V

Trace and write the letter.

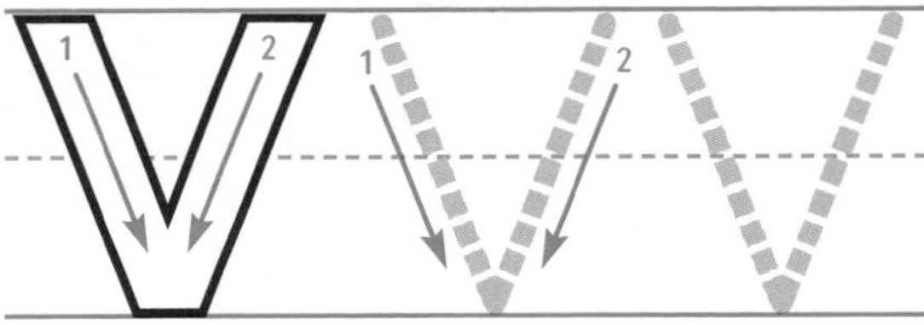

Circle the ones that begin with V.

Dog

Van

Vase

Trace and write the letter.

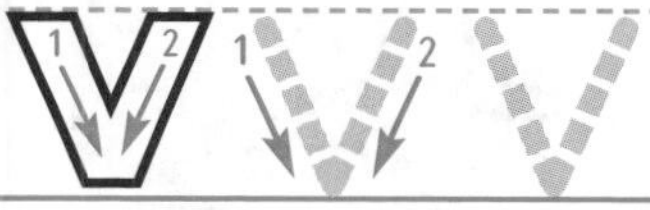

Circle the ones that begin with v.

violets

balloon

vegetables

A Nice Umbrella

Connect the dots from M to U.
Color the picture.

A Very Big Valentine

Connect the dots from h to v.
Color the picture.

Capital W

Trace and write the letter.

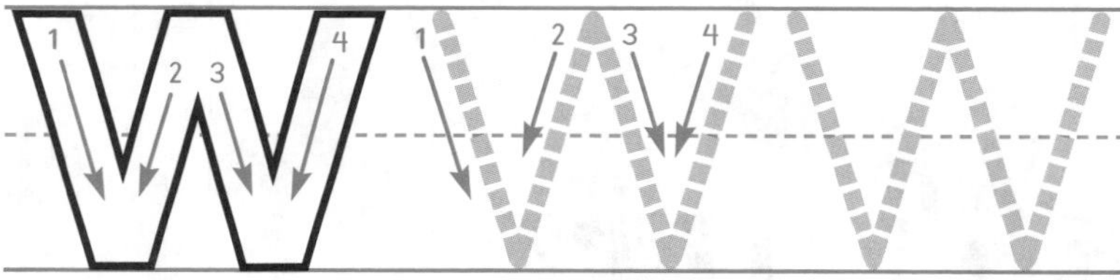

Circle the ones that begin with W.

Wolf

Woodpecker

Snake

Trace and write the letter.

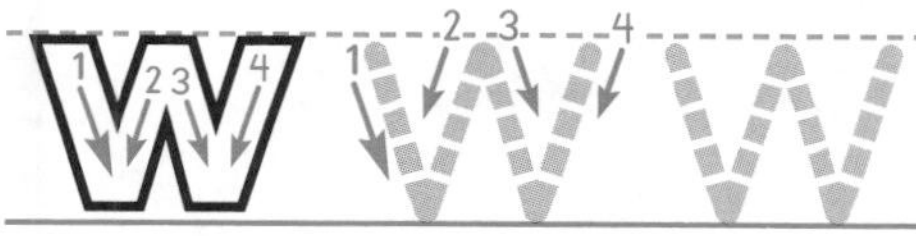

Circle the ones that begin with w.

apple

walrus

window

Capital X

Trace and write the letter.

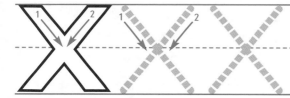

Circle the one that begins with X.

X-ray

Elf

Trace and write the letter.

x x x

Circle the ones that begin with x.

fish

xylophone

x-ray

Trace and write the letter.

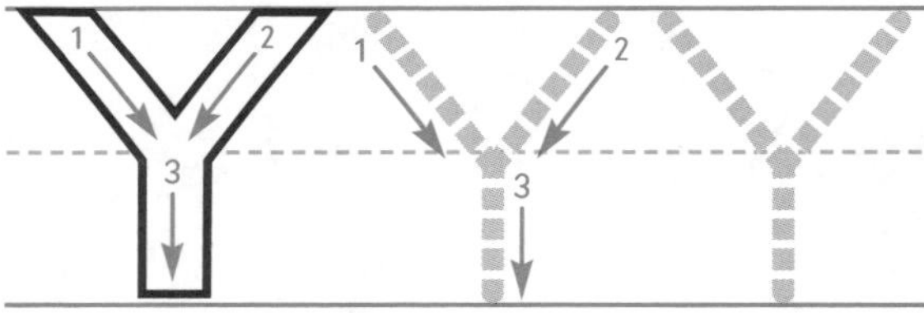

Circle the ones that begin with Y.

Yarn

Fox

Yo-yo

Trace and write the letter.

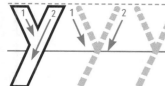

Circle the ones that begin with y.

yellow

yak

parrot

Trace and write the letter.

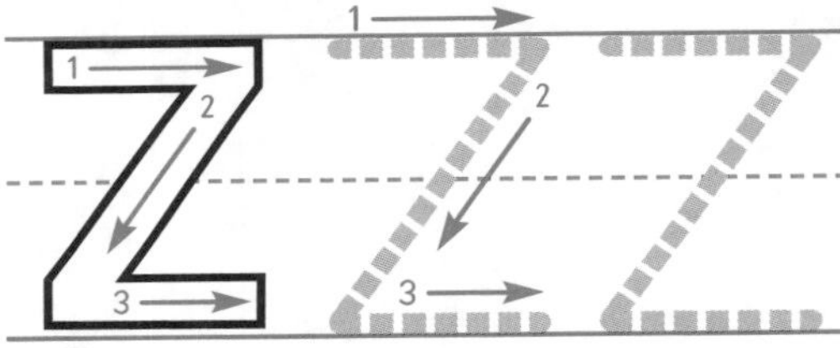

Circle the one that begins with Z.

Zoo

Supermarket

Trace and write the letter.

Circle the ones that begin with z.

zipper

baby

zebra

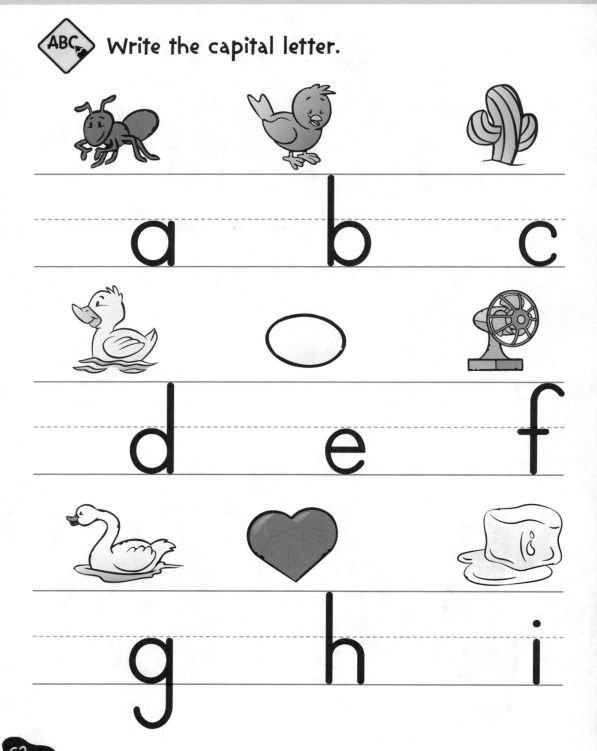

Write the capital letter.

a b c

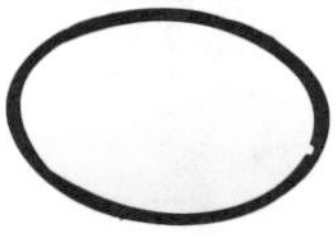

d e f

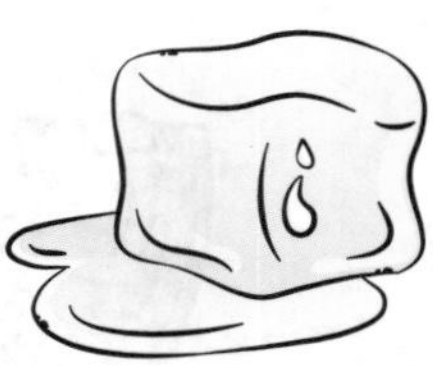

g h i

Write the capital letter.

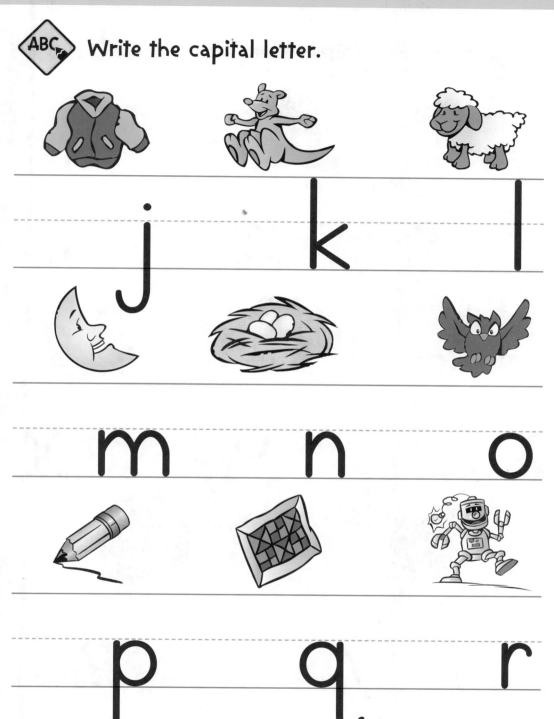

j k l

m n o

p q r

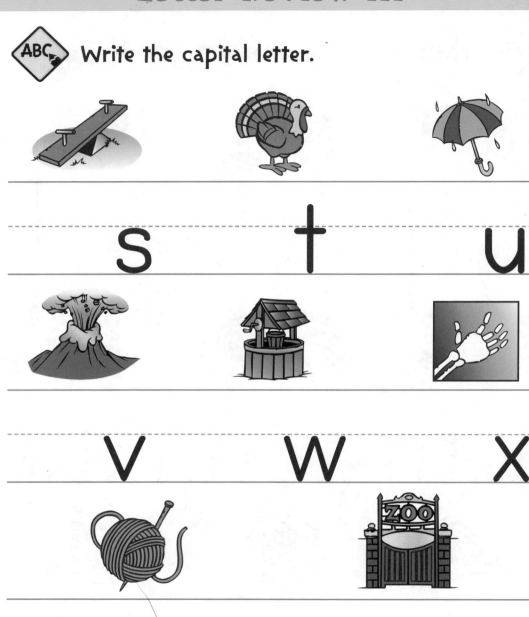

Write the capital letter.

s t u

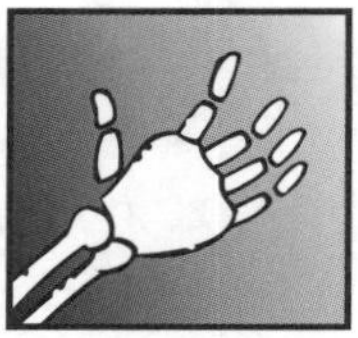

v w x

y z